C0-ASM-132
CADMUS
BOOKS

OOTOOK, YOUNG ESKIMO GIRL

by

LYN HARRINGTON

Photographs by Richard Harrington

When Ootook was ten, she could chisel a hole in the ice and catch fish to eat, for the family was always hungry, but she wanted to have her own trap-line in order to catch fox and trade their pelts. She already knew how to scrape the pelts and dry them. Ootook also had fun with her friend Mary, whose father ran the trading post. The girls built their own snowhouse and carried their dolls in the backs of their parkas just as the Eskimo women do. Ootook's family, like other Eskimo families on this frozen north region, constantly battled for food, not only for themselves but for their dogs — their only means of transportation. The caribou was the most valuable because it not only provided food, but the best clothing, tents and blankets. Read this book about how Eskimos live, illustrated with pictures of real people.

* * * *

Dewey Decimal Classification: 919.8

About the Author and Illustrator:

LYN AND RICHARD HARRINGTON are a husband-and-wife writing team. Mr. Harrington is Canada's outstanding documentary photographer. Mrs. Harrington goes with her husband on most of his trips, and consequently has a wide knowledge of the Arctic and its people. She has been a children's librarian in the Soo and in Toronto, and is the author of many articles and stories, as well as a junior novel, *Stormy Summer*. Although they live in Toronto, Richard Harrington travels constantly, covering thousands of miles by canoe, dogsled, horse, tractor train and bush plane. He wrote *The Face of the Arctic*, and his photographs are highly rated.

Ootook in caribou skin clothing, with her toy pipe between her teeth.

OOTOOK
Young Eskimo Girl

by Lyn Harrington
photographs by Richard Harrington

1964 FIRST CADMUS EDITION
THIS SPECIAL EDITION IS PUBLISHED BY ARRANGEMENT WITH
THE PUBLISHERS OF THE REGULAR EDITION
ABELARD-SCHUMAN LIMITED
BY
E. M. HALE AND COMPANY
EAU CLAIRE, WISCONSIN

Library of Congress Catalog Card Number: 56-10030

This edition lithographed in U. S. A. by Wetzel Bros., Inc., Milwaukee 2, Wisconsin

CONTENTS

ILLUSTRATIONS

OOTOOK: *Young Eskimo Girl*

The trading post of Padlei on the shore of Kinga Lake — store, Mary's house, Ootook's house. Dogs are tied up at the foot of the hill.

Chapter One

OOTOOK GOES FISHING

"Umh! Umh! Umh!" Every time Ootook brought the ice chisel down, it jolted the breath out of her. Breaking away the new ice in the waterhole was hard work. Besides, the ice chisel was heavy, and taller than the ten-year-old Eskimo girl.

"Umh! Umh!" Chips of ice flew in every direction as the iron thudded down. Ootook was too hot, in spite of the cold wind whistling across the frozen lake. She shoved back the hood of her fur-lined parka and took off her big mittens.

Then she started to work again. She was glad she didn't have to chop through all five feet of ice that covered Kinga Lake. "Umh! Oooh!" The chisel broke through the last layer of ice, and dark water welled up through the hole.

Ootook dropped to her knees and scooped the slush out of the way. Then she unwound her fishing line. "The waterhole is a good place to fish," she thought. "Perhaps something will be caught."

Her fishing line was of braided caribou sinew, tied to a wooden frame called a "jigger." She had a tiny scrap of white cloth on the hook to attract the fish. Bait was not necessary in this Arctic lake.

Now the hook and line sank down through the hole and out of sight. Ootook began to hum a wordless song to attract the fish. She moved the jigger up and down, up and down, steadily, until she felt a slight tug on the line. A fish! Immediately, Ootook began to wind the line around the jigger, so that it wouldn't tangle. Up, up, up, it came, dripping icy water and with bits of slush clinging to it.

Ootook's black eyes sparkled as she pulled out a trout nearly a foot long. She quickly took it off the hook, and tossed it to one side. At once the fish froze stiff in the February air.

She hoped someone had seen her catch that fish! The sunlight dazzling on the snow made her squint as she looked toward the few buildings of Padlei. But no one stirred around the Hudson's Bay Company post, at the store, the trader's house, her own home, or the tiny chapel. A few Eskimos moving around their snowhouses were too far away to notice.

"Well, my mother Eegie will be glad, anyway," Ootook said to herself, "even if it is not a very large fish."

She returned to jigging up and down, up and down, humming softly. In the clear cold air she could hear children's voices from the igloos, and the occasional howl of a husky dog. Nearer was the constant whir of the windchargers behind the trader's house. They charged the batteries for the radio-phone on which the trader could talk to people far away. Now the wind felt cold again, so she pulled the hood over her beret, and then all sounds were muffled.

Ootook at the waterhole, where she has caught two fish by jigging the line up and down.

Another tug at her line. Ah, the fishing was good at this waterhole! She jerked the line upward. Yes, it was a fish. Quickly she hauled up the line, winding it around the jigger. But it came so easily she guessed the fish must have escaped. Sure enough, the hook came up empty.

Ootook was neither cross nor disappointed. That often happened, and she had learned to be patient. "It cannot be helped," she always said, using the old phrase of the Eskimo people. She just let the line down again, and began jigging up and down as before.

As she kneeled there, her arm moving steadily, her eyes roved over the snowy country. Other people might think the region west of Hudson Bay bleak and flat, but Ootook couldn't imagine any place more beautiful or interesting.

It was hard to tell where Kinga Lake ended and the shore began, since both were covered with snow. Far off, she could see a dark smudge. That was a grove of spruce trees where Kretsuyuk, her father, got wood for the settlement. He hauled it by dog-sled across the lake to the trading post.

"But we Padleimiuts are 'People of the Willow Thickets,' not of the spruce grove," Ootook thought contentedly.

A sudden jerk on the line nearly pulled the jigger out of her hands. That must be a big fish! She hoped this one would stay on the hook. Up came the fish,

Ootook's house, showing the stormporch.

Tudlik breaks fresh ice with the ice-chisel to get water, while Shaunuk looks on.

struggling to escape. Ootook could see through the slushy water that it was a large trout, the biggest one she had ever hooked.

She jumped to her feet for the last hard pull. Then she heaved the big fish out onto the snowy ice of the lake. The trout flopped a few times, then lay still.

She was satisfied. This was enough food for the family's next meal. So she picked up the two fish and the jigger and started for home. She was part way up the slope when a woman and a child in fur clothing came out of the box-like stormporch. It was her aunt Tudlik and her four-year-old cousin Shaunuk. They lived at Ootook's house, and so did her uncle Nanow.

Ootook couldn't help grinning whenever she thought of Nanow. He was always telling stories or making up songs, and he kept the family in gales of laughter when he was around. He would have made up a song about Ootook's big fish, only he was away looking after his fox traps. His line of traps made a big circle south of Padlei, and he was often gone for a few days or even a week. Sometimes he came home without even one fox; other times he was lucky enough to get seven or eight. Tudlik would clean the pelts and Nanow would take them to the store to trade for food and clothing.

As she met them on the trail, Ootook saw that Tudlik had a water pail in her hand, while Shaunuk carried the dipper.

"What a big fish!" her aunt exclaimed. "Ootook

catches fish as if she were a grown woman." Tudlik spoke in the polite Eskimo way.

"Me carry fish!" Shaunuk demanded, throwing the dipper to the ground.

As usual, Ootook had to laugh at her cousin's Eskimo baby talk. So she gave Shaunuk the small fish to carry. Auntie didn't scold as she picked up the dipper. Shaunuk would soon learn not to be careless or bossy, just as all Eskimo children did.

Ootook followed the little girl up the path to their house. "A little brown bear is what you are like," she said laughing. She knew fur clothing had to be loose for warmth, but Shaunuk's clothes were made to grow in. Shaunuk didn't care what she looked like. She just plodded up the hill carrying the trout, then thrust it at Ootook, and ran back to the waterhole.

In the porch, Ootook hung the jigger on the pail, and carefully brushed the snow off her clothing. If she allowed the snow to stay on her clothing indoors, it would melt, and then freeze the next time she went out. Holding both fish in one arm, she opened the door and closed it quickly behind her, to keep out the biting wind.

The warm house was filled with the aroma of meat stewing over a low fire. Ootook's mother sat on the wide sleeping bench that ran across the end of the room. Attached to her copper headband were loops of beads that swung as she looked up, smiling. Ootook admired those beads very much, and the ones on Eegie's clothing.

Ootook and her cousin Shaunuk wear warm clothing made from caribou skin when they play outside in the Arctic weather.

"Wood is needed," her mother said gently.

She never gave orders. Ootook could fetch wood for the stove if she liked. She could work or play, whichever she pleased. But more and more lately she found she liked to help. It made her feel grown up. A quick glance under the stove showed only two sticks of firewood lying there on the bare boards.

Over beyond the trader's house the logs were standing on end like tent poles. That was to keep them from being covered with drifts of snow. Ootook's father Kretsuyuk had cut one log into short pieces to fit their stove, and she piled up a big armful.

Kretsuyuk could do anything, Ootook always boasted. He worked for the Hudson's Bay Company, doing all sorts of jobs, and lived in a house supplied by the company. He carried water for the trader's family. He fed the husky dogs and kept their harness in repair. He piled up snowblocks around the store and houses to protect them against the cold wind. He cut firewood in the spruce grove, and sawed it into stove-lengths.

As she went back along the path, Ootook caught a movement at the kitchen window of the trader's house. That was Mary, her best friend. Her nose was pressed against the frosty glass, and she waved to Ootook. Ootook couldn't wave back, because of the firewood, but she smiled, thinking of the fun they always had playing in the afternoons.

As soon as she dumped the wood beside the stove, Ootook pulled off her parka. It was made of caribou skin, the lightest, warmest fur in the Arctic, and was covered with cotton cloth. Often she wore another parka over it, with the fur turned outward.

She tossed her red beret onto the sleeping shelf behind her mother. Her hair was tied up in little braids behind her ears, straight black hair that wouldn't hold a curl. Her fur pants had suspenders of braided yarn that crossed over her woolen sweater.

"A girl is hungry," she said, lifting the lid of the pot. There was always something cooking slowly. Ah, good, it was caribou meat, and she picked out bits of it with her fingers.

"Bannock is in the food box," Eegie reminded her.

Ootook tore off a chunk of this heavy bread, then sat down beside her mother, nibbling on the doughy bannock. She watched Eegie tie knots at regular intervals in a thong of caribou hide. This would be sewn onto a leather boot-sole.

She was still eating when Shaunuk and Tudlik came back with the water. Little bits of ice tinkled as her aunt poured water into the kettle. It would be a long time before the tea was ready, so Tudlik sat down on the bench, too, and took up her sewing. She used sinew, for the long fine muscles from the caribou's back made very strong thread.

Shaunuk scrambled up on the bench behind them, and began to tug at Ootook's hair, until she caught sight of her mother's braids. Soon she had opened a whole braid, but her mother didn't mind. Tudlik,

Indoors, Shaunuk opens a braid of her mother's hair, but Tudlik doesn't mind. She keeps on sewing.

like other Eskimo parents, loved children and never scolded them.

Shaunuk finally grew tired, and sat down on the bench. She couldn't keep her eyes open, and soon fell asleep. Her mother gently drew a caribou skin blanket over her. She was just braiding her hair again when the door opened and closed quickly.

Mary entered in the Eskimo way, without knocking, and was ready to play with Ootook.

Chapter Two

PLAYTIME AT PADLEI

"Welcome," Ootook called. Mary spoke and understood Eskimo as well as Ootook. She crossed the room to the sleeping bench, pressed her nose fondly against Eegie's, and shook hands with Tudlik.

Then, turning to Ootook, she asked, "When are you coming out to play?"

"Soon," said Ootook. "A girl is learning to sew now."

Mary pulled off her parka and, as Ootook had done, tossed it and her beret onto the sleeping bench behind her. Her fair head was close to Eegie's shoulder, as both girls watched the shiny needle poke in and out of the leather.

Eegie laid the knotted cord around the boot-sole in circles, and caught it with the strong thread all along its length. Ootook looked down at her boots. Their soles were of polar bear skin, and so were Mary's.

"Polar bear skin makes a good sole," Eegie told them. "It is warm and keeps a boot from slipping on the hard snow. But if one has no more bear skin, then this knotted cord is good."

One day, she, too, would sew boots, Ootook decided. But right now she had had enough, and wanted to go out into the bright sunlight. She decided to

Mary and Ootook watch Eegie sew a knotted cord to a boot-sole.

Caribou skin clothing is very slippery, as Mary and Ootook discover. Kret-suyuk smiles at their fun.

wear her new white beret, and pulled it on over her braids. Mary did the same, and both wore fur parkas, snug and warm for outdoor play.

"Let's slide down the hill beside the lake," Mary suggested.

Ootook grinned, and trudged happily after her.

The snowdrift, piled up on the shore of the lake, seemed very high when they looked down from the top.

"Here goes," Mary shouted, and she went slithering down the slope, feet first. Ootook was right behind her, and hit the bottom a moment later. Laughing, they ran back to the top of the snowdrift, and slid again and again. Their caribou skin clothing was extremely slippery, and they whizzed down the little hill as if it were pure ice.

"Now watch me," Mary called. She threw herself down on her stomach, and away she went. Ootook was just as quick, but she went down head first. At the bottom was a big pile of snow loosened by their feet. Ootook plunged right into it, and came up sputtering, her mouth full of snow.

Mary waited, laughing, and exclaiming, "Ootook, your cheeks are as red as your old beret!"

Ootook laughed just as hard, even though some of the snow had gone down her neck.

Kingmik, one of the sled dogs, heard their shouts and wandered to the top of the snowdrift to watch them. He seemed to think it was great fun, and his thick tail wagged slowly. Most of the dogs around

Kingmik won't pull the sled, no matter how much Ootook coaxes him.

the post were tied up, to prevent them from fighting or stealing food. But Kingmik was almost a pet, although he was a true Arctic husky, strong and short-tempered.

"Perhaps Kingmik will pull us on my sled," Ootook cried. She had no trouble harnessing a dog, especially one as gentle as Kingmik. The dog leaped around happily when he saw the harness. He liked pulling with the rest of the team. But when he realized that he was expected to pull the sled alone, he howled the sad long wail of the Arctic husky.

Ootook coaxed, "Come on, Kingmik, get going." But Kingmik sat back on his tail, and looked stubborn. She scolded him. It made no difference. She cuffed his ears, but still he wouldn't budge.

"I'll tie a string to a bone, and drag it in front of him," she said at last. "Then you'll see him move."

Kingmik moved very fast indeed. He made a mighty leap forward to snatch the bone. That jerked the sled, and Mary tumbled off into the snow. Ootook dropped the bone at once when Kingmik forgot to be gentle.

"Ah, well, it's no use," said Ootook. "Kingmik will not pull us. Perhaps we should play with our dolls."

The girls ran up the hill to their homes to fetch their dolls. Mary's had real hair, and could close its eyes when she laid it down. Ootook's was a sturdy one with fair hair painted on its head. Both were Christmas presents from Mary's father.

They put the dolls in the back of their parkas,

in the way that Eskimo women carried their babies. Above Ootook's shoulder peeked the little fair head, and behind Mary's head was the black hair of her doll. They had made little suits of fur for the dolls, just like their own fur clothing. So they dressed and undressed them, sang them to sleep and wakened them.

"It would be nice to play house," Mary said after a while. "Why don't we build a snowhouse of our own? You could get your father's big snowknife, and we can cut out the blocks ourselves."

That would be fun, Ootook thought. At once, she ran to get the snowknife, the doll bouncing up and down in the back of her parka. No one said, "Don't cut yourself!" or even "Be sure to bring that knife back when you're finished with it." She was expected to know such things without being told, and she did.

The snowknife was nearly two feet long, and Ootook poked around to find hard snow, suitable for building blocks. She and Mary had often seen snowhouses being built, but they didn't realize how much work it was.

At last they found just what they wanted, and Ootook cut a large block. Mary set it into position on the snowy ground. Ootook cut another block, which Mary placed beside the first, leaning both of them inwards a little. Then they changed jobs. Soon the bottom row of snowblocks was in position in a circle, but they were getting hot and tired.

Just then Ootook caught sight of Pana, a boy who

Ootook and Mary at the entrance to their igloo carry their dolls in the back of their parkas as Eskimo women carry their babies.

Pana cuts hard blocks of snow for the playhouse with a big snow knife.

lived in one of the igloos beyond the store. He often went hunting and trapping with his father, and now he was carrying home some flour for his mother.

"Pana," called Ootook, "help is needed to build this igloo."

Pana came over at once. He dropped the bag of flour onto the ground, and picked up the snowknife. "It is a good start," he said, when he saw the work they had done.

He began to cut snowblocks, and the two girls piled them into position, Ootook on the inside, Mary on the outside. When it came to the last block, Pana cut it too small. He handed it to Mary, and she put it into the opening at the top. It fell right through into Ootook's face, and snow got down inside her parka again.

Mary and Pana shrieked with laughter, and Ootook laughed, too. So they tried again. Again the snowblock was too crumbly, and it smashed down into Ootook's face. This time it didn't seem quite so funny.

"It cannot be helped," said Pana. "A boy is a poor igloo builder. Perhaps Kretsuyuk will cut the last block."

Away went Pana, and presently he returned with Ootook's father. Kretsuyuk was surprised to find that Pana and the girls had made a very fair snowhouse. He knew exactly what size to cut the block to fit the opening. He lowered it into position himself, and this time it didn't fall through on Ootook.

"A girl is locked in the igloo," said Kretsuyuk, laughing as he handed the snowknife to Pana. "And a house needs a door."

Pana grinned, and at once cut a low doorway through two blocks of snow. That block now became the door itself. Kretsuyuk brought an empty wooden box from the store for furniture.

Pana picked up his bag of flour, and went along home. The girls played in their snowhouse, singing their dolls to sleep and waking them again.

After a time Ootook said, "My child is hungry. Some milk is what she needs." She giggled, knowing perfectly well that dolls could not eat or drink, but she liked to pretend. She ran home and brought back a baby bottle full of powdered milk and water.

"My doll wants tea," said Mary. "Let's go and ask my mother for some."

They pushed the block of snow away from the entrance, and climbed the hill to Mary's house. Ootook didn't go there very often, and her eyes were wide with wonder as they entered the kitchen.

It was far too hot for her comfort. The house was full of the fragrance of baking gingerbread, and the spices tickled her nose and made her sneeze. From another room, she could hear the chatter of the radiophone, where Mary's father was talking to the Hudson's Bay Company trader at Eskimo Point.

"Of course you may have a pot of tea," Mary's mother told them.

The kettle sang softly to itself on the back of

the stove and, in a few minutes, it was boiling. Mary put a little tea into the pot and poured hot water over it. She got out two enamel mugs and a few hardtack biscuits from the cupboard.

Mary's mother opened the door and Mary carried the pot of tea out to the snowhouse, while Ootook carried the mugs and biscuits. No sooner had they settled inside than Mary said, "We should invite Pana. He helped us build this playhouse."

So she crawled out of the low doorway, and shouted at the top of her voice, "Pana! Pana! Come and have tea!"

Pana was playing hide-and-seek among the igloos with some other boys. They all raced over. Ootook emptied the milk out of the baby bottle into the tea, to make it go further, and Mary poured it into the mugs. They took turns drinking it. The hardtack biscuits shattered like soda crackers, but the boys didn't waste a single crumb.

When the tea was all gone, they drifted back to their game, and the girls went on playing house. Finally Mary said, "Let's trade dolls. My little girl wants to live with you for a while. She would like to learn Eskimo ways."

Ootook tried to keep her face straight. "My child has light hair like yours. She would like you for her mother." Then they both broke out laughing. But when they crawled out of their playhouse, the black-haired doll went visiting in the back of Ootook's parka.

Hardtack and tea in the snowhouse make Ootook and Mary feel right at home with their dolls.

Ootook pretends her doll can drink milk just as a real baby does.

The short February day had ended, and it was already dark outside. A wind was rising and whistling around the house when Ootook reached home. Laughter rang out from the inside, and at once she knew her uncle Nanow had returned.

He was part way through a story, telling of an Eskimo trapper he had met a few miles from Padlei. As Ootook opened the door, Nanow was saying, " . . . going to show me all the things he had got in trade for his furs, especially his new gun. Then the silliest look came over his face. 'The gun must be on the counter of the trading post still! It seems I forgot to take my new gun with me!" Everyone laughed at Nanow's way of mimicking the Eskimo. "So then he had to come all the way back to the post to pick up his gun. What a hunter that one is, to forget a gun in the excitement of buying other things!"

Kretsuyuk and Eegie listened intently, their eyes twinkling as Nanow talked. Tudlik seemed very proud of her husband, and of the four white foxes he had brought home with him. They lay in a heap in one corner of the room. Shaunuk had already gone to bed, and soon Ootook too was snuggled beside her under the caribou skin blankets.

Every pelt has to be stretched on a narrow board until it is dry.

Chapter Three

FUR FOR THE TRADING POST

Eegie and Tudlik were again at work when Ootook awakened next morning. Tudlik carefully cut and peeled the skins off the foxes Nanow had brought yesterday. Then she stretched each pelt on a long narrow board, inside out. After that, she would scrape the fat off the hide, using her *ulu,* a small curved knife. She hung each stretcher on a nail outside, where the skins dried in the sun and wind. Tudlik always helped Nanow this way, and sometimes she cleaned the skins brought to the store by other trappers.

For a few minutes, Ootook lay in bed listening to the women talking. Then, realizing she was hungry, she wriggled out of the caribou skin blankets and into her clothes. She helped herself to some of the fish left over from last night.

As she ate, she watched Eegie and Tudlik at work. It looked so easy, the way their strong hands and knives moved over the skins. Tiny shavings of fat curled from Eegie's *ulu,* and the stiff caribou hide became as soft as velvet under the constant scraping. Once it was all soft, she could cut and sew it into clothing or bedding.

Sometimes Eegie scraped the skin until it was as white as the snow on Kinga Lake. Clothes made

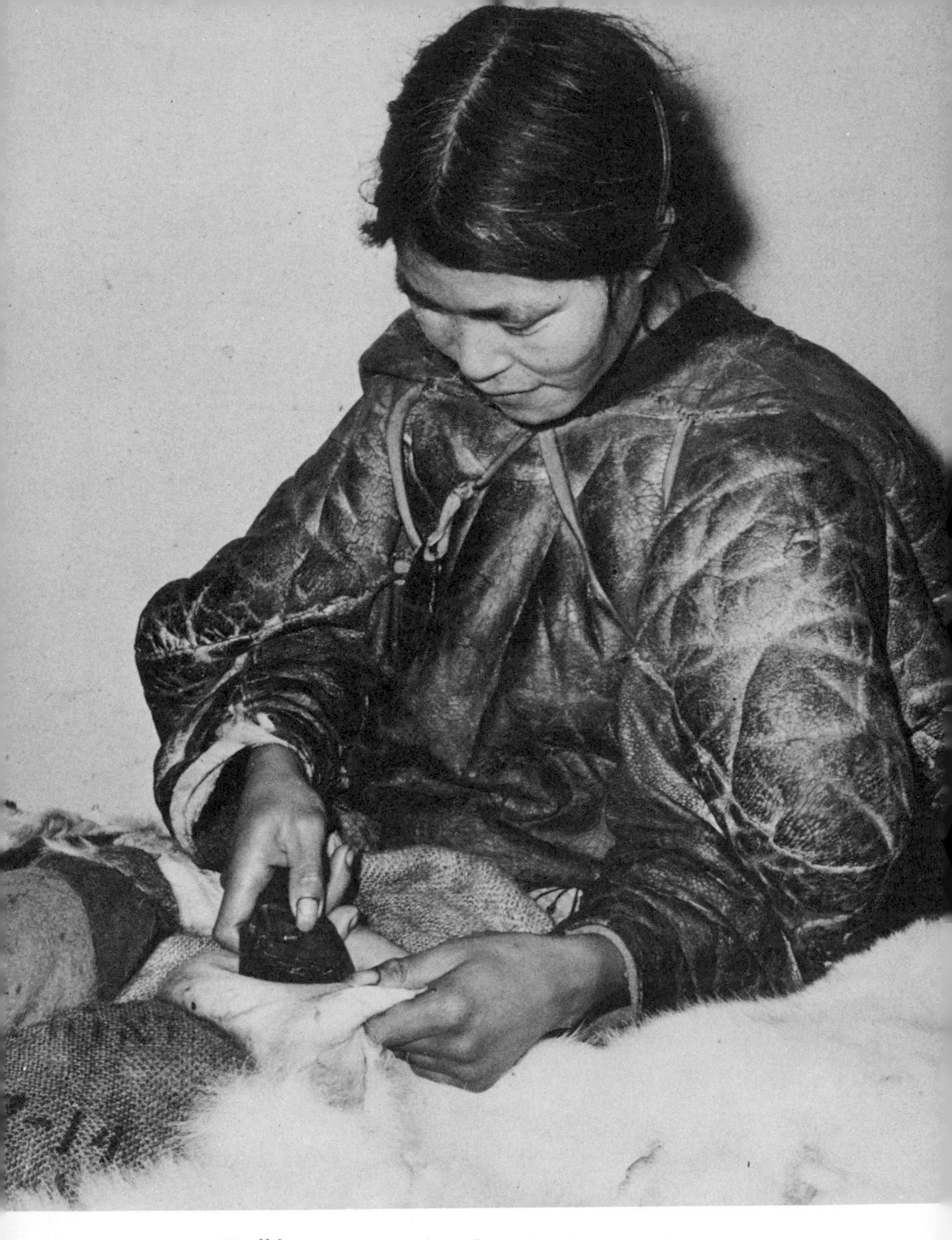

Tudlik sitting on the sleeping bench, cleaning white fox pelts for the trader.

from that were kept for special occasions, but after a while when the skin got dirty, they could be worn every day. Mary had a beautiful white parka, decorated with beads, and Eegie promised Ootook one just like it some day.

If Ootook learned to scrape hides, perhaps she might get one sooner!

"A girl would like to do that, too," she said, after a while.

Eegie nodded. "It seems Ootook is ready to learn the crafts of women. A little woman could start on a fox pelt. On the shelf is another *ulu.*"

Ootook found the *ulu,* and noticed that the edge was very dull. A sharp blade in a beginner's hands might cut the skin. Tudlik gave her one of the fox pelts stretched on a board. No one had to tell Ootook how to scrape the pelt. She had seen it done so often, she knew just what to do. The smelly fat came off in large greasy gobs, later to be fed to the dogs.

She kept at it all that morning. She couldn't work as quickly or as neatly as either of the women, because she didn't have their experience. Sometimes she laid down her knife and watched them. Their hands were so skilled, she thought she would never, never learn to do it as well.

Finally she sighed deeply. "To trap foxes must be more interesting, surely, than to clean the pelts."

"Yes, indeed," Eegie agreed. She had a few traps set out on the tundra beyond Padlei, which she

Ootook starts out for the store, with half a dozen fox skins for the trader.

visited about once a week. Every now and then she brought home a fox.

Ootook wondered how old you had to be to have a trapline. But then, where would one get traps? She had nothing to give the trader in exchange for a single trap.

"Ootook has worked very well," said her aunt, getting up from the bench. "Perhaps she would like a change. Would Ootook carry those dried fox skins to the trader's store?"

Would she! Ootook's black eyes snapped with pleasure. There was nothing she would like better. The store was a wonderful place, and she loved any excuse for going there. The shelves held such pretty packages, and some of them smelled so nice.

Tudlik had half a dozen skins ready to go back to the trader. She turned them right side out, so that the soft fluffy white fur showed. "What use are fox skins to anyone?" she exclaimed, as she often did. "This fur is not warm enough for clothing, not like caribou. The white man is very strange to give food in exchange for such worthless fur."

Ootook pulled on her parka and was ready to go before her aunt stopped talking. She didn't even bother with a beret, in her excitement. The white fox skins were not heavy, but they were so long that the fluffy tails dragged on the floor. Ootook hitched them over her shoulder, smiled back at her mother when she saw Eegie's smile of approval, and started out.

She had just gone a few steps, when she suddenly remembered that she liked to look her best whenever she went to the store. She rushed back into the house, and pulled the string off her braids. Her hair fluffed out around her face and, for a while, her straight black hair held the kinks. She put on her beret, and was satisfied.

The still air inside the store was bitterly cold. Every nail in the wall stood out, like a bump coated with frost. Coal was costly and wood scarce, so none could be spared to heat the Padlei store. Actually, the cold didn't matter, since the trader and all his customers wore fur clothing.

Ootook looked around the store, enchanted. The shelves were piled with food in red, blue, and yellow packages. There were ropes, and chains, and tin pails, aluminum kettles and leather, alarm clocks and steel traps, soap and tobacco and toys, including dolls. There were also bolts of cloth in bright colors and pretty patterns. How could anyone ever choose among all these beautiful things, Ootook wondered.

The trader was busy with two customers. An Eskimo trapper had brought in several foxes, and was now making his purchases, with his wife at his elbow, reminding him. On the counter lay some aluminum coins. As the Eskimo bought tea, the trader put one coin back into a drawer. He bought some tobacco, and another coin clinked in with the first. He bought flour, a bright silk scarf, and some sugar.

The Eskimo woman shows her new kettle to her friends, while Ootook looks on.

One of the women has all kinds of decorations on her parka, and Ootook sees that one of them is from an alarm clock.

There was only one large coin left on the counter.

The woman nudged her husband, and pointed to a shiny kettle.

The trapper turned to Mary's father. "That kettle would be nice to have."

"Yes," the trader agreed, and he reached the kettle down from its shelf. Then he dropped the last coin back into the drawer. "That is all for now."

Both Eskimos smiled happily, and gathered up their purchases. It had taken them over an hour to make up their minds.

Now it was Ootook's turn. She managed to heave the skins up onto the high counter, with the trader's help. "That is a big load for a small girl," he said laughing, and reaching for his account book. Ootook wanted to tell him that she was nearly a woman, but she was too shy. Then the trader wrote down how much he owed Tudlik for cleaning the pelts. It would be paid in store goods, for money was of no use to these Eskimos.

Outside the store, Ootook saw that the customers had not gone back to their igloo yet. They were showing their purchases to their friends. Several women had gathered around to admire the new kettle, and the owner let Ootook, too, lift the lid and look inside. One woman had a great many ornaments dangling across her parka, which Ootook thought very nice. Why, she even had some shiny wheels out of a broken alarm clock.

While she was looking at them, the dogs at Padlei

Kretsuyuk was busy drilling a hole in a slat for the dog-sled when the policeman's team arrived. He uses an old-fashioned bow-drill.

began to howl. They scented a strange team of huskies coming across Kinga Lake. Ootook could see the small dark blob on the white snowfield, but it was too far away to guess who it might be.

The trader came out of his store to look. Mary and her mother appeared at the kitchen window, where the frost was melted from the glass. The Eskimos crawled out of their igloos. Ootook's father was drilling a hole in a piece of wood, and he screwed up his eyes, as he studied the sled in the distance.

"The policeman comes from Eskimo Point," he said after a minute. Kretsuyuk had very sharp eyes, and he knew every dog team.

"You're right, of course," said the trader. "I heard on the radio-phone that he would come some time this month. He must have had a good trip. I'll tell my wife to expect a guest. The special constable will stay at your house, Kretsuyuk, as usual."

Ootook was thrilled. It was good to have a visitor, almost as good as going on a visit yourself, she thought, and she loved company.

Gradually the dot grew larger, and presently the Royal Canadian Mounted Policeman and his Eskimo helper reached the trading post. The fur around their hoods was covered with frost, and even their eyebrows were white. It had been an easy trip, they said as they shook hands with everyone, and the team was strong. Indeed, the well-fed dogs carried their tails curled high over their backs, and were eager to fight every dog in Padlei.

Well-fed, healthy, alert dog of the Canadian Mounted Police.

But the special constable wouldn't allow that. He staked out a long chain, and fastened each dog separately, so they couldn't fight. Then he took dried fish from a sack, and tossed one to each dog. The dogs swallowed their supper with a single gulp, then curled up in furry balls to sleep. Their tender noses were tucked under their thick tails, to keep them from being frostbitten in the night.

The special constable carried the policeman's gear into the trader's house, then took his own sleeping bag over to Ootook's house. He shared his food with Kretsuyuk's family, and ate some of theirs.

That evening, the Padleimiuts living in the igloos, and others who were in to trade, crowded into Kretsuyuk's house. The special constable always brought news of other Eskimos, and had stories to tell of his travel adventures, and of the white man. They sat on the floor and on the sleeping bench, each puffing away at a soapstone pipe, until the air was blue with tobacco smoke.

Chapter Four

THE POLICEMAN BRINGS NEWS

"Few caribou have I seen in the country," the special constable told them. "It is a good thing we brought plenty of supplies from Eskimo Point. Otherwise, we and the dogs would have gone hungry many times."

"Yes," Kretsuyuk agreed, "the caribou are everywhere scarce at this time of year."

The wanderings of the caribou were the most important thing in the lives of these Eskimos. Every spring, these antlered deer migrated north in herds, using age-old routes. Each autumn, most of them wandered south again on the familiar paths. The Eskimos knew where to find them, and each hunter tried to store up enough meat to feed his family and his dogs through the winter. Thus the caribou herds provided food and warm clothing and bedding.

But some years, for unknown reasons, the caribou took different paths. The Eskimos waited for them in the usual places, and when they didn't come that way, the hunters and their families starved. Only a few animals remained on the Arctic plains through the winter, and it took a good hunter to provide enough food.

"Most Eskimos live at the seacoast where they do not have to depend on the caribou in spring and fall," said the special constable. "They go out in boats

Karluk and Ootook in the trading post with Mary's father.

to hunt the seal, the walrus, and even the white whale. Plenty of food is there, if a man has skill."

"Ugh, seal meat is good only for dogs." Nanow screwed up his face into an expression of disgust that made the others laugh. "One summer, I went to the coast to fish, and ate some. I do not like it."

"And what do we Padleimiuts know of boats and seals?" asked Karluk, a trapper. "We hunt the caribou, as the Old Ones did before us. In past times, our people only hunted. They did not trap foxes to buy store goods."

Karluk's camp was twenty miles away across the Barrens. He had brought in several foxes to trade at the store for supplies. "One caribou a day I need for my family and dogs, and the meat in my cache is very little. I am a poor hunter and trapper."

He didn't really mean it, Ootook knew. Only a successful Eskimo could talk like that.

"Karluk is the best hunter and trapper among the Padleimiuts," Kretsuyuk said firmly. "This year is bad, yes, but it has happened many times before that the caribou went a different way."

"Few skins have I," Karluk went on, "for few foxes sought my traps. One will need credit at the trading post to feed the family, and other mouths, too, are hungry in my camp."

"But there is the Family Allowance," the special constable pointed out. "With it you can get traps, guns, food, clothing, or fishing nets. That helps to take care of one's family, and one does not have to trade fox skins for it."

Ootook was so interested that she forgot for the moment that it was not polite for Eskimos, especially children, to ask questions directly. Her voice seemed to pop out of her. "What is this Family Allowance?"

Instantly, every eye turned toward her, startled. Ootook wished she had not spoken. Never again would she ask a question, she determined, never in her whole life!

But the special constable was glad to explain, as he had done many times before, when interpreting for the policeman. "It is a gift from the Canadian government to every child in the country, every month of the year," he said.

Then this government, whatever it was, might give her some fox traps, Ootook thought. But she would have to find out without direct questioning.

The next day, the policeman began his visits to every household in Padlei. He asked all kinds of questions and he wrote down the answers in a large book. The Eskimos didn't understand what it was all about, but they answered truthfully.

He asked about the hunting and the trapping, because he had to see that the Eskimos obeyed the game laws. If the people were starving, he had to supply some food for them. He asked how many people lived in Padlei, and how many came there to trade. Out of a thousand Caribou Eskimos, about forty lived at the trading post, and about thirty families traded there. The policeman asked if there had been any crimes, such as stealing or killing. There were none.

Then he came to Family Allowance, to make sure that every child got its share. He wrote down the name of every person at Padlei, and their relation to one another. Finally, the policeman reached Kretsuyuk's house on the hill. He wrote down the names of Kretsuyuk and Eegie.

"Ootook is your only daughter?" he asked.

"Yes."

"Your real daughter, or adopted?"

"Her real father is our son Aklunak," Kretsuyuk said at once. "He lives farther north, and he gave his first baby to his parents, according to the old custom of our people. There was no child in our house, and he has other children."

Ootook was surprised, but not shocked, to learn that Kretsuyuk and Eegie were her grandparents, not her father and mother. That didn't change their love for one another.

Then why was the policeman frowning? He spoke crossly, and the special constable interpreted, "There are too many such adoptions. She should be with her parents."

"The policeman is angry," Ootook thought. "It must be a bad thing not to live with one's parents. But how does one find them?"

Then she heard Kretsuyuk explaining with dignity. "This is often done. Aklunak and his wife have

The Family Allowance poster in the trading post, written in English and in Eskimo writing.

other children to care for. We have none. What is a home without a child? Our way is best."

The policeman gave a big sigh. "Perhaps it is, but this is the way the Canadian government wants it. You'll have to straighten it out. Her parents are alive, and the Family Allowance will help them to look after her."

Then he turned the page of his big book, and began to ask Nanow questions about Shaunuk.

Did that mean they would send her away? Ootook wondered. Would she have to live with people she didn't even know, away from all the people she loved in Padlei?

After the policeman had gone, Kretsuyuk noticed her sadness. He said, "The white man likes to keep his big book in order, and he gets worried easily. He does not understand that this is a tradition of our people." Then he pulled a piece of willow out of the pocket of his shirt, and began cutting it with his knife. His eyes twinkled when he looked at Ootook, who watched him make a hole down the center of the stem.

Eegie sat on the sleeping bench, quietly smoking her pipe, and clouds of tobacco made a wreath around her head. Somewhere Kretsuyuk found a piece of gray soapstone, which he carved into a small bowl. Now he drilled a hole in one side, and stuck the hollowed bit of willow into it.

"Here is a pipe for Ootook," he said, smiling, as he handed it to her.

Ootook forgot her sadness at once. She kept the toy pipe clenched in her teeth even when she and Eegie went outside for more wood, and all afternoon when she played with Mary.

"It's a real pipe, but a little one," she explained to Mary. "One could smoke it as Eegie smokes hers."

"Not without tobacco in it," Mary said, laughing. "Where did you get it?"

"Kretsuyuk made it for me. He is my grandfather, you know, not my father," Ootook told her. "The policeman was cross that I do not live with my own father and mother. But I do not even know them."

"It is not the custom among white people to give away children, even from a large family," Mary explained. "But my mother says the Eskimo way is sensible. Still, most girls would want to know their family, even if they didn't live with them. I would."

But Ootook wasn't curious. She was perfectly content with her life at Padlei. Or she would be, if she had some fox traps.

Next morning, she saw Karluk carry his white foxes into the store. She knew it would take him a long time to decide what he wanted most. And while the trader was waiting, she would ask him for the government's gift.

"This Family Allowance," she began, in a low voice, "it would be good if the government would give a girl a fox trap."

"Why, Ootook, do you want to be a trapper?" asked the trader, smiling down at her. "I'm sorry, but

Ootook's little pipe would smoke like Eegie's if it had tobacco in it. Eegie wears wooden sun goggles.

the government gives the gift to the parents for the child. It is a gift of credit at the store. You bring in your father or mother, and they can get a trap for you if they like."

Ootook thought he meant her real parents. Well, then, she would simply have to find them, and tell them about the government's gift. It would be hard, without asking questions, but she would find a way.

Just then Karluk returned to the counter. He asked for shells for his rifle, tobacco, kerosene for his primus stove, and needles for his wife.

"You may have other things, too," said the trader, "because of the Family Allowance. You have four children?"

"Two sons and two daughters," Karluk said.

The trader laid out some more aluminum disks on the counter. "Then you can have that much more in goods."

Karluk hesitated. Then he said, "More food is needed, that is true. Well then, tea and sugar and flour and some of that powdered milk."

As the trader placed these items on the counter, Karluk stuffed them into a bag. He had already iced the runners of his sled, and now he tied the bag in place. He was harnessing the dogs, when Ootook had the idea, "Why not go with Karluk? Maybe my father lives at his camp."

Aloud she said, "One would like to visit your camp, and play with your daughters."

Karluk presses the brake made of caribou antler into the snow.

Chapter Five

NEW FRIENDS

Karluk showed no surprise when Ootook invited herself to his camp. He often took a sudden notion to go visiting, and all Eskimos liked having company.

Eegie didn't object, either. "But one must not go empty-handed." At once she began to collect hardtack biscuits and dried fish for Ootook to take with her. Then she added small packets of tea, sugar, and flour. "Nanow can fetch you home when he goes that way to tend his traps."

By the time Karluk had harnessed the dogs, Ootook was ready to leave with him. Her cheeks were red with excitement. The huskies howled and yelped, anxious to be on their way. Mary and Pana and the other children milled around the sled, shouting, and some of them hopped on for a little ride. They soon jumped off, and ran back to their homes.

At first the trail wound through a small valley, where the wind had blown the snow off the rocks. Now the dogs ran silently. Ootook, perched on the sled, could hear nothing but the squeak of the runners on the hard snow. Whenever her feet grew numb with cold, she jumped off and ran alongside for a while. Karluk put on his wooden sun goggles to protect his eyes against the glare on the snow.

After a few hours he shouted to the dogs and the

sled stopped. He pressed a brake made of caribou antler into the snow, and said, "Tea would be good." He lit the primus stove while Ootook gathered snow to melt for tea. The hot tea warmed them both, and the hardtack tasted better than ever before.

Then they were off again across the snow-covered land. Ootook had not paid much attention to the direction, but now she noticed that their shadows fell to the east. Then they must be heading to the southwest! Kretsuyuk had said her parents lived to the north. Ootook shrugged her shoulders a little. "It cannot be helped," she thought.

About the middle of the afternoon, a sudden movement off to the right caught her eye. She half turned to call Karluk's attention to it, but he had already seen it.

"Caribou," he said quietly, but his eyes were excited. "One caribou." He halted the dogs, and pressed the brake into the snow.

The caribou had seen them, too. It stood there at a distance, its branched antlers looking just like those of a reindeer. It seemed more curious than frightened, but it would run at the least alarm. Although it was a long distance away, Karluk kneeled on the snow, and slowly raised his rifle. The shot sounded very loud to Ootook as she sat motionless on the sled. Then she saw the caribou topple over on the snow.

There was no holding the dogs. They knew what had happened. Karluk flung himself on the sled as the team dashed toward the fallen animal. The brake

Karluk crouches on one knee on the snow, taking careful aim at the caribou.

dragged behind, bouncing along on the ridged snow-drifts.

Karluk's face wore a happy expression. He wouldn't boast, of course, but Ootook knew that it had been a very good shot. That caribou meant food for his family and the dogs. It took only a few minutes for him to skin the dead animal and load the meat on the sled.

By now, the short day was ending, and it would soon be dark. The dogs pulled harder than before, for they were going home, carrying their supper with them. In a couple of hours, Ootook saw several faint lights ahead in the darkness, a gentle glow that came through ice windows and snow walls.

A few dogs in camp lifted their heads and gave yelping howls, which Karluk's team answered at once. The sled stopped beside a large low igloo, and Karluk's two sons rushed out. Immediately all the loose dogs in camp surged around them. Food was so scarce that the dogs were left untied to hunt for anything they could find.

In a moment, the sled dogs and camp dogs were mixed in a snarling, brawling mass. Karluk had his whip out, and was laying about with the handle, when one dog, hurtling through the air, knocked Ootook to the ground. At once the dog turned on her, savagely, and only her thick fur clothing saved her from its teeth. Karluk was there in a flash, to beat the dogs away.

Ootook got up shakily. She wasn't hurt, but she

Karluk's igloo is made of snow walls with a roof of caribou hide. One of his sons uses a knife to scrape the ice window free of frost.

was badly frightened. They all knew that in the confusion of a dog fight anything on the ground was likely to be torn apart, whether friend or foe.

The dog fight didn't last long, for the camp dogs were weak and Karluk's dogs were tired. Soon peace was restored, and the boys helped Karluk feed the team. The dogs snarled and growled over the bones, and not a scrap of meat remained when they curled up in the snow to sleep.

Then they carried the gear down a few steps, through a low doorway and into the igloo. Ootook and Karluk's two daughters at once beat the snow out of their outer clothing, and spread it to dry on a wooden rack. As soon as it dried, Karluk's wife would sew up the rips the dogs had made in Ootook's clothing.

Other Eskimos of the camp crowded in to welcome Karluk home, and shake hands with the visitor. Karluk gave each a small piece of caribou meat, saving most for his own family, as was the custom.

Ootook had never seen an igloo like this. It had snowblocks for walls, but the roof was made of caribou skins sewn together, and propped up with poles. The one window was made of a sheet of ice cut from the lake. A soapstone dish of melted caribou fat was the only fire, and a pot bubbled over the flickering rag wick.

Everything from the trading post had to be examined and admired. The food Ootook brought was added to the family supply, and everyone shared in

Karluk and his family. Keenalik looks up into her mother's face.

it. Ootook thought she was starving! The lunch of tea and hardtack seemed a long time past. But in a few minutes, she was dipping biscuit into the broth of the stew from over the fire, and picking out bits of meat from the bowl on her lap. The warmth of the igloo, after the excitement of the day, made her so drowsy that she nearly fell asleep as she was eating.

"Ootook can sleep beside Keenalik," said Karluk's wife.

Keenalik, the nine-year-old girl, giggled a little. Then both girls pulled off their clothes, and snuggled on the sleeping bench under blankets of caribou skin.

"Tomorrow we can play," Keenalik whispered.

Ootook meant to answer, but she was too tired.

In the next few days, Ootook and Keenalik played together in and out of the igloo, hauling younger children around on small sleds. They carried water for the household, and were careful not to spill any on the steps. Ootook liked the crunching sound they made when they scraped the frost off the ice window with a knife. Keenalik's special job was to bring in fresh snow to spread on the floor with a stick. That made the floor cleaner than if she had swept it.

Very often, Keenalik's mother and older sister worked on fox pelts, just as Tudlik did at Padlei. They all helped one afternoon, when Karluk and his two sons were out hunting. Keenalik scraped slowly and clumsily, and Ootook was surprised at her own skill. But then Keenalik was younger, she realized.

"Ootook scrapes a fox skin very well," Keenalik's mother said.

How glad she was that she had already learned that lesson!

"The trader gives more goods for pelts that are well cleaned," she went on. "Women can help their husbands by scraping the fox skins well." She looked at her older daughter with meaning, and smiled.

"My sister is to be married in the spring," Keenalik whispered, "to a good trapper."

Ootook wasn't surprised that a young trapper liked Keenalik's sister. She thought her the most beautiful woman she had ever seen. "A woman can help to feed the family by fishing," Ootook said shyly. Yes, she thought, and by running her own trapline, too!

Keenalik was getting tired of scraping skins. "Tell us a story, Mother. With the string."

Her mother laughed, and laid down her work. She took up a long piece of string, knotted the ends together, and slipped the loops over her fingers in a queer fashion. "String figures help you to see the story," she said, smiling.

Ootook could hardly follow the swift movements of her fingers, as she made cats' cradles with the string. She made a polar bear, then a rabbit, then the flame of a little fire, and the snow drifting across the land. Sometimes she used her teeth to pull one loop of the string over another finger. A large figure

Keenalik loves stories told with string figures for illustrations. This shows two caribou.

slid across the two bars of string, followed by two smaller ones.

"That's the caribou, running away from two wolves!" Keenalik shouted. "Now tell us the story about the thunder."

Her mother nodded, and this is the story she told.

In the earliest times, there was no such thing as stealing. But then one day it happened, during a drum dance, that a boy and his sister were left alone in a house. There they found a dried caribou skin and a stone for making fires. These they stole. But hardly had they got them home, when a great fear of their fellows came upon them.

(Here Keenalik's mother pulled the strings, and Ootook could see the two figures running away with the stolen hide and the firestone.)

"What shall we do to get away from everyone?" asked the girl.

"Let us turn into caribou," said the boy.

(And the string figures turned into two large caribou.)

"But the people will kill caribou," the sister protested.

"Then let us turn into wolves," said the brother.

(Now the string figures shrunk, and crept across the two bars of string between her hands.)

"The people will kill wolves," said the sister.

"Then let us turn into foxes," said the brother.

(And the string figures grew smaller, and raced

across the string bars. Ootook couldn't take her eyes off those clever fingers that could make pictures out of a piece of string.)

"The people kill foxes," said the sister again.

"Let us turn into rabbits," said the brother.

(And so the story went on and on, each part illustrated with some new figures. Keenalik and her sister had long ago laid aside their fox pelts.)

Finally the brother said, "Let us turn into something that people cannot catch and kill. Let us turn into thunder and lightning, and then the people will not be able to catch us."

And so they turned into thunder and lightning, and went up into the sky. When there is thunder and lightning now, it is because the sister rattles the dry caribou skin, and the brother strikes sparks from the firestone.

Ootook sighed happily, "Oh, that was a good story. One would like to make those string figures." So Keenalik's mother taught them both how to loop the string around their hands, and how to catch it with their different fingers.

"Boys do not learn to make string figures," Keenalik said. "Their fingers might become clumsy when they shoot the rifle, and so they would not be good hunters."

Just then they heard the sound of running footsteps, and the boys burst into the igloo. "Look!" shouted the younger brother. "He got three ptarmigan. Already my brother becomes a great hunter."

Karluk's son gets three ptarmigan one day, and becomes a young hunter.

The older brother looked down at his feet. It was not polite for him to brag about his skill, but he enjoyed hearing someone else boast for him.

"My brothers do not play with string, you can see," said Keenalik proudly.

When Karluk came in, he had to tell the whole story of how they had stalked the ptarmigan from the sled. "So small and white these birds are against the snow, that one could hardly see them. But my son has sharp eyes, and a steady hand. Three ptarmigan he shot, and there is food for everyone."

Ootook had noticed that Karluk and his sons always got a larger share of the food than the women. This was right, she knew, because hunters were the most important part of an Eskimo family. They had to go out into the cold and travel far to obtain food. Now she thought Keenalik's brother looked taller than when he went out. He was not just a boy any longer — he was a young hunter now.

Very soon afterward another hunter arrived. Nanow had followed his trapline in that direction and now came to fetch Ootook. He enjoyed such visiting, and was very welcome. An owl had sprung one of his traps, another had a rabbit in it, and only two held foxes.

"At least, the rabbit can be eaten," Nanow said, joking over his poor luck on the trapline.

Chapter Six

ON THE TRAPLINE

Ootook felt as though she had been away for a long time, and she expected many changes. There was only one, and she noticed it the moment they reached Padlei late the next afternoon.

"Look, Nanow, there is smoke from the chapel," she cried. "The Father must have come from Eskimo Point."

Nanow grinned happily. "Many visitors this winter. In old times, one scarcely saw a white man, and we had to travel many miles to a trading post."

Nothing had changed in the little white house on the hill, where everyone was glad to see her back. Eegie greeted her with a quick brush of the nose, and Ootook pressed her nose to Shaunuk's.

Then she rushed out again and over to the chapel. Mary stood watching the priest saw wood. As each piece fell from the sawhorse, Mary and Ootook took turns carrying it into the chapel. In spite of the fire in the small stove, the chapel was still cold, for it had been buried in snow for months. The priest would hold a service next morning, as he always did when visiting Padlei.

The little chapel was crowded with Eskimos at the early service, including Ootook. She didn't want to miss anything, even though she didn't understand

The tiny chapel is surrounded with snow, and Mary and Ootook take turns carrying in the wood which the priest saws off a log.

what the priest was chanting. But she liked the sound of it, and admired his lace-trimmed cassock with the gold-embroidered cloth over it.

"The Father wears beautiful clothing," she said later to Mary. "He must be very rich, though he is not a trapper nor a trader."

"No, he is really very poor," Mary explained. "People give gifts to the church, and the church gives the Father what he needs."

"A girl would like to give him something," Ootook said wistfully. But what did she own, except the toy pipe? And Shaunuk had broken that while she was visiting Karluk's camp. She glanced toward the store. "A fox skin would be a nice gift."

The clothesline was crowded with bunches of fox pelts, hung out to air in the bright windy weather. They swayed in the wind, and Ootook saw that the fine white fur stood out clean and fluffy. Kretsuyuk and the trader took them down again in the later afternoon, and piled them up in the storeroom.

That evening as they sat around on the benches, Ootook said hesitantly, "A girl would like to trap white foxes."

"One cannot catch foxes without traps," said Kretsuyuk, surprised. "And to get traps, one must give the trader something."

Ootook admitted she had nothing to trade.

Eegie smiled gently. "My daughter does not yet know how to set a trap."

"I will show you," said Nanow. "Some day."

Kretsuyuk and the trader hang their bundles of white fox pelts out on the line to air.

Ootook thought to herself, "At least I can learn how to set a trap, and be ready when I get one of my own. Nanow can teach me tomorrow."

But in the morning, when she awakened, Nanow had already left for his trapline. Ootook decided to follow him. She told Eegie: "He cannot be far ahead. Kingmik can catch up with him and Nanow will show me how to set a trap." Eegie nodded and said: "Yes, that would be good."

Without waiting for breakfast, Ootook harnessed Kingmik to the small sled, and this time he was willing to pull her. He was eager to be with the rest of the team, which was not very far ahead on the trail.

In places, the wind drifted snow over the trail, and Ootook had to walk ahead looking for Nanow's sled tracks. In the flat treeless land, and on a day without sun, she couldn't tell which direction he was heading. If Nanow and his six dogs had been traveling in a straight line, Kingmik could never have caught up with them. But Nanow had to stop frequently to set traps.

He was cutting away a block of snow when they caught up with him. Nanow was surprised, but he smiled at Ootook.

"A girl wishes to learn to set traps," she told him, with a grin. She hoped he wouldn't be cross with her for following.

"Ootook is determined to be a fox trapper." He laughed. "Well, first you must know that the Arctic fox is very curious. He likes to examine every hump

Ootook harnesses Kingmik to her small sled, to follow Nanow.

Nanow was cutting a block of snov to cover the fox trap when Ootool caught up with him.

of snow. So beside a mound, like this snow-covered rock, one places the trap. One puts a layer of snow over it, and the fox has to scratch to get at the bait."

"Perhaps a girl could set the next trap," Ootook suggested timidly.

Nanow shrugged his shoulders. Then he started off on his sled, and Kingmik pulled Ootook along right behind. Presently Nanow stopped his dogs again. "Perhaps the new trapper can find a good place to set a trap here?" he suggested.

Ootook looked around. Over there was a rock just like the one farther back. She looked at her uncle, and he nodded his head. Then he handed her one of his traps. Ootook carried it and the big snowknife over to the rock, and cut away a slice of hard snow just as Nanow had done. The space left was the right size for a fox trap.

Nanow handed her a little piece of rotten fish for bait, and she laid it carefully on the trap. Now she had to open the jaw of the trap and set it, so that the fox's scratching would spring it shut. The trap was set, and Ootook trimmed the block of snow very thin, and laid it on top, hiding the trap from sight. Then she turned away, very pleased with herself. As she did so, she bumped into the handle of the snowknife, and it fell on top of the trap.

SNAP! Ootook jumped as if the trap jaws had closed on her, the sound was so loud in the still air.

Nanow grinned, as usual. "A girl is lucky that it was not a hand or foot caught there."

For the first time, Ootook thought about the Arctic fox which might be caught in the trap. How frightened it must be when the trap sprang shut! But her pity did not last long. Eskimos had to trap the white fox and kill the caribou in order to stay alive themselves.

Ootook did the job over again. "It is not hard to set a trap," she said.

"No, not hard. But traveling around the trapline is hard, especially if nothing is in the traps," Nanow said. "A girl could have a short trapline around the trading post, like the one Eegie has. But now I must go on."

He started off on his big sled, and his dogs were glad to be on the trail again. Kingmik wanted to go with them. Ootook shouted at him, and tried to make him go back to Padlei, but Kingmik wouldn't listen to her. Soon they had overtaken Nanow again.

He understood her problem at once. "Well, Ootook will learn about following the trapline," he said smiling. "We will leave your sled here, and harness Kingmik with my team."

Kingmik was happy to be harnessed with the other dogs, although the team snarled at first. But he pulled his best, and the dogs soon got used to him. Nanow's big sled whisked over the snowy ground, with Nanow and Ootook both riding.

"My new trapline," Nanow told her, "goes in a circle, and we will pick up your sled on our return from the north."

Nanow helps the woman with her load of twigs to her skin tupik. Small spruce trees beyond.

North! Why, then, perhaps they might be near Ootook's father and mother. Steadily the team hauled in the same direction. Ootook could tell from the ridges of the snowdrifts. Suddenly the dogs speeded up, and peering over Nanow's shoulder, Ootook could see a woman walking across the snow. Her heart beat a little faster.

The woman looked very strange from a distance, and no wonder the dogs had mistaken her for a caribou. Branches of willow stuck up from her shoulders out of the large bundle she carried. Willows might grow five or six feet high in sheltered valleys, but on the windy Barrens, they grew along the ground. Willow twigs and dry branches of tiny spruce trees were the only fuel in this part of the Arctic.

Nanow halted the sled beside the woman. In a minute, he had tied her bundle to the sled, and she hopped on beside Ootook. They soon reached her tupik, a tent made of caribou skins sewn together. A thin thread of blue smoke rose from a tin stovepipe. Inside the tupik, an old woman cackled a welcome. She huddled close to a little stove cut from an oil drum from the trading post. The woman fed some twigs into the stove, and placed a kettleful of snow on it, and tossed in a few tea leaves.

They sat around in friendly silence, broken only by an occasional remark. Ootook thought the tupik was very crowded, with even four people in it. Then the woman said she was sorry she had no sugar for the tea, so Nanow fetched a little from his sled.

As they sipped the scalding tea, the woman began to talk.

"My husband is out hunting," she said. "Ah, this is the worst time of the year, with our meat supply nearly finished and the caribou so scarce. Farther north, one is told, there were even fewer caribou last fall."

Nanow said thoughtfully, "Farther north. That is where Aklunak lives. It's a long time since he was at Padlei."

"Aklunak!" Ootook repeated. "Why, that is my father's name. It would be nice to see him, perhaps." Her eyes widened with excitement.

Nanow looked at her for a long time. Then he said as if it didn't matter, "One could visit Aklunak. It is only a little out of my way."

Without any further farewell, Nanow and Ootook left the little tupik, and off they went to the north. North, to where Aklunak lived among the spruce trees.

A storm was blowing up when they reached the spruce grove where Aklunak lived.

Chapter Seven

FOOD FOR THE HUNGRY

Even though Nanow had decided to go visiting, he didn't forget to set traps wherever he found a likely spot. So they were not much farther north when darkness fell.

It took nearly an hour to build an igloo for the night, even with Ootook filling all the chinks between the snowblocks with loose snow. It was not much larger than her playhouse back in Padlei.

Nanow always carried a frozen haunch of caribou meat, enough to feed him for the two or three days he was out on the trapline. Now he had to share this with Ootook. The sled also held a sack of dog-feed, dried fish taken from Kinga Lake last summer. Nanow fed the dogs, while Ootook melted snow for tea.

On the snowbench inside the igloo, Nanow spread first a mat of twigs, then laid his caribou skin bedding on top. Ootook of course, had no blankets, and Nanow gave her half of his. So neither had enough, and both shivered during the night, even though they kept their fur clothing on.

Breakfast next morning was another mug of tea and hardtack biscuits. Then they were ready for the trail once more. Outside, Nanow looked worried. "It smells like a storm," he said. "Perhaps one should return to Padlei."

Only the tiniest wrinkle of Ootook's nose showed her disappointment, but her uncle noticed it. "Oh, well, we will be in Aklunak's log house anyway."

It was dusk again, and a rising storm made it hard to see ahead when they reached a frozen lake. An ice chisel sticking up through the snow indicated the family's waterhole. Then the dogs floundered into the soft snow of the spruce grove, and stopped before a little log hut almost buried in the drifts.

Not a husky howled or snarled a greeting, and no one came out of the dark hut at first. Nanow had tied up the dogs and unloaded the sled before the wooden door opened and an Eskimo stepped out. "That must be my father," Ootook said to herself, as he shook hands with them both. "His voice sounds very tired."

Before going into the hut, she helped Nanow feed the dogs. They threw one dried fish to each, the last of their dogfeed. But they could be back in Padlei the next night, if they pressed on hard all day. Ootook's father, Aklunak, said in an astonished voice, "One still feeds dogs!"

Then Ootook understood that her father was not just tired. He was weak with hunger.

But he helped carry their gear into the hut. How dark it was! The logs chinked with moss did not reflect light as snow walls did. And the floor of the

Inside the dark hut Ootook found her Father and Mother, two little sisters, and a small brother. Aklunak chops some meat from Nanow's frozen caribou haunch.

hut was black earth, not the wooden floor Ootook was used to, nor the clean snow floor of an igloo. A battered oil drum shed a little heat, and the only light came from a stub of candle set on an old tobacco tin.

Ootook's mother, Yarrak, sat on the sleeping bench, in the proper place for the woman of the house, and reached a hand forward to greet Ootook in the customary Eskimo way. Ootook also shook hands with a sister about seven years old, with a little brother of three, and even with a year-old baby on her mother's shoulders. It was nice to find a family, she decided.

But when Nanow explained that Ootook was their eldest daughter, she saw dismay in her parents' eyes. They thought she had come to live with them, and were alarmed.

"There is no food," her father said miserably.

There wasn't anything in the house to eat except a bit of flour and baking powder for bannock. With his axe, Nanow chopped bits of meat off the caribou haunch, and they crunched it between their teeth. It tasted good, and soon sent a feeling of warmth through their bodies. They didn't mind waiting while Yarrak mixed up a bannock, and baked it on top of the stove.

Then Aklunak spoke again. "A man has had very bad luck in hunting. Last fall, one waited at the usual places, but the caribou did not come. One could not put aside meat for the winter. It could not be helped."

Nanow nodded. If an Eskimo hunter missed the big herds in the autumn, he had to hunt very hard to keep alive during the winter. And if there were few animals in his part of the Arctic, he might easily starve to death. But Nanow reminded Aklunak of the Family Allowance at the trading post.

"One thought of that," Aklunak admitted, "too late. Every day, one hoped to get a caribou. None came. So then one could not leave because there was nothing to feed the dogs and they died."

Ootook thought to herself, "It is not so very far. One could travel by dogs in one day, Nanow said, so it would not have been too far to walk."

But her father was speaking again. "A man could have walked to Padlei, but how could I leave my wife and the little ones with no food? The other families here moved away, hoping to find better hunting. Yarrak and the children could not walk to the trading post, for we are all weak. One son has already died, and there will be another child to feed soon. Besides," he ended with a shrug of despair, "the Family Allowance is only a small amount to feed so many."

"Aklunak has not been to Padlei for many months; therefore his credit will have grown to a large amount," said Nanow. He looked politely at the candle, not addressing Aklunak directly. "Moreover, the policeman wishes you to have the Allowance for Ootook, as well."

Ootook knew then that she would not get the fox

trap after all. The credit at the trading post would all be needed to feed the family.

Aklunak lifted his head more hopefully. "How will one get to the trading post?"

"This place is no good for hunting this winter," said Nanow thoughtfully. "Aklunak would do better to set his traps around Padlei. It is true, there are no caribou there either. But at least one will not starve there. Tomorrow let us all go on my sled. My dogs are fresh and not tired. If we start early, by night we should all be in Padlei."

"Yes, tomorrow we move," Aklunak agreed. "A man feels stronger already with food inside him."

The stub of candle was now very low, and before they finished eating, it guttered wildly and went out. The log hut was in darkness, except for tiny points of light that showed through holes in the drum-stove. There was nothing to do but go to bed. Nanow added his blankets to the sleeping bench, and soon Ootook was lying beside her sister who coughed all night long.

The bedding was scant at best, for Yarrak had used some of the skins to make clothing for her husband. The remaining caribou hides were worn hairless in spots, and felt damp with grease and black earth ground into them from the floor. Ootook twisted and turned trying to get warm. Even though she was wearing her fur clothing, cold chills ran down her back. All night the wind howled through the spruce grove, and every now and then a tree split with the frost, making a sound like gunshot.

Morning made little difference in the cabin. It had no window, though some light came through a small opening in the roof of caribou hides. Worse than the darkness and the coughing of the family, was the blizzard raging outside. None of them dared go out even for more firewood.

"Cannot go to Padlei today," said Nanow. "Tomorrow will do." He sounded cheerful, but Ootook knew he was disappointed. Occasionally he looked out the door but had to admit the storm was as bad as ever.

"It will last for three days," said Aklunak. "These blizzards always do."

No one spoke of the food shortage, but everyone thought about it. Ootook knew the caribou meat would last only one day, and tomorrow they would boil the bone. There was no more feed for the dogs, of course. They would get nothing to eat until they were back in Padlei. In the Arctic, dogs had to go without food when men were hungry.

For three days and nights, the wind howled around the tiny hut in the spruce grove, slapping hard particles of snow against the walls. In the darkness, with only a little warmth from the stove, Ootook thought about her home in Padlei. How lucky she was to live with Kretsuyuk, who received regular wages from the trading company. A hunter was never sure of getting enough food for his family.

The dogs are covered with snow after the blizzard, but their thick coats protect them from the cold.

Every morsel of food was gone by the second night. Not a particle of meat or a crumb of hardtack or a spoonful of flour remained. Fortunately, Nanow had brought plenty of tea. They could not get to the waterhole in the storm, but there was snow in abundance. The hot, sweetened tea warmed them, and filled their aching stomachs. Ootook was learning what hunger really meant.

On the fourth morning, she awakened from a chilly slumber to a strange silence. The storm was over.

She could hardly wait to start back to Padlei. With her uncle's team, they could just make the trip in one long day, even with the extra load. Ootook and her sister would have to walk a good deal, and so would Nanow and Aklunak. But even so, she was anxious to be off, though by now her head felt a bit light from hunger.

Nanow's voice came out of the dark silence. "It might be good to make a small hunt today. Perhaps there are caribou farther off from the camp, which we can follow with the dogs."

"It may be so," Aklunak agreed.

In a few minutes, Nanow went out to harness the dogs. Ootook slipped into her outdoor clothing to join him, glad to get out of the dark, smelly hut into the clean, fresh air. At first, she couldn't see the dogs, they were so covered with snow. At the sound of Nanow's voice, they got up stiffly, and Ootook had to laugh to see the crown of snow on Kingmik's head.

With the broken chisel Ootook chops away the ice over the waterhole.

Now Aklunak emerged, ready for the hunt. His warmest clothing was a greasy parka, dirty in spots, and with patches of fur worn off. Aklunak carried his rifle, and a little bag at his waist held his ammunition. Ootook could see the outline of two bullets – the last he had. Nanow noticed it, too, but politely said nothing.

After, the hunters left, Ootook decided to get water from the lake. It took such a lot of snow to make even one cupful of tea. She got the battered bucket from the corner, and set off. It was easy enough to find the waterhole, although the blizzard had filled the path with fresh snow. But of course the waterhole was frozen hard, and Ootook had to chop it free of ice. She thought, a bit crossly, that her sister might help her with this work. Then she remembered that none of the children had clothing warm enough for outdoors.

The ice chisel thudded down onto the snowy lake, and chips of ice flew into the air. It reminded Ootook of fishing through the ice at Padlei. But it was even longer before she chopped through to the water.

As she carried the bucket back to the cabin, she thought again about the hunters. What if they didn't find even one caribou? Or what if they couldn't get near enough to shoot it? That would mean another day without food. She made up her mind. It was a woman's work to fish, if possible.

"But we are not fish-eaters," Yarrak told her,

when she asked for a line and jigger. "We live on caribou meat."

"Fish is not as good," Ootook agreed, "but at least it is food. If Nanow and Aklunak bring home caribou meat, the dogs will be glad of the fish."

There was no jigger in the house, nor fishing line. However, Yarrak found some sinew thread which Ootook braided into a line. The thread would have been used for sewing long ago, if there had been any skins to make into clothing. Ootook tied one end of her line to a stick of firewood, and wound the line around it. That would have to do for a jigger.

A fish hook! She had forgotten a most important piece of equipment. Yarrak couldn't help her. Nanow was gone. Ootook felt discouraged. As she leaned back against the frosty door, something poked into her back. A nail. The frost had pushed several nails part way out of the wood. Maybe she could bend one into a fish hook, she thought. So she wiggled the nail until it was loose enough to pull out. It was about five inches long, and crooked..

Ootook didn't worry about that. First, she had to file a notch into the nail, so that the fish would not slip off the hook. It took Yarrak some time to find the file, in the confusion and darkness of the hut.

Then Ootook went outdoors, where she could see to work. After patient filing, she managed to cut a barb into the nail and sharpen the point. Then using the head of the axe, she carefully bent the nail into the shape of a fish hook.

As soon as she caught the trout, she hurried back to the log hut carrying the fish in her arms.

At last, she was ready to return to the waterhole.

The hut didn't provide even a scrap of white cloth to attract the fish, much less any bait. But Yarrak told her no one had ever fished in the lake, so perhaps she would be lucky.

She was. Almost immediately, Ootook pulled out a salmon trout. By now she was too cold and hungry to stay out any longer. Picking up the fish before it could freeze, she ran back to the hut.

"Oh, my," exclaimed her mother in admiration, "Ootook provides food. Can fish be good for people as well as dogs?"

Ootook didn't take time to answer. She just chopped the fish into sections, and proved how good it was by eating some of it at once. She gave her mother the piece near the tail, the best part of the fish. The other children snatched up pieces, and began to chew. It was wonderful to feel strength and warmth returning.

Ootook was secretly very pleased with her success, but it would be bad manners to say so. Soon she said carelessly, "Perhaps there are more fish in this lake."

"It may be so," agreed her mother, very proud of her eldest daughter.

That afternoon, Ootook pulled seven trout out of the lake that had never known a fish hook before.

Chapter Eight

WELCOME HOME TO PADLEI

Nanow and Aklunak came into the log hut wearily, and Ootook knew at once that they had not brought any meat with them. She was glad her fishing had been successful. For now the trout were boiling over the fire, and the hut was filled with a steamy aroma.

"Ah," cried her uncle sniffing the air, "Ootook has been fishing, one can tell." Ootook glowed with pleasure.

"There is also enough for each dog to have half a fish," she said, trying to sound casual. "It is no trouble for a girl to feed them." She pulled on her outdoor parka again, and went outside. She wanted to make sure that Kingmik got his fair share of the food. The dogs leaped to catch the frozen fish she tossed. Then, with a yawn, the tired huskies curled up in the snow.

One of them snored loudly while Ootook stood there looking up at the Northern Lights. Long fingers of light played across the clear cold sky. They were like lightning . . . no, like curtains . . . or no, she decided, they were more like fox pelts fluttering in the wind. But they changed every moment, and tonight they seemed low enough to touch.

"That means tomorrow will be good weather for traveling," Nanow told her, when she went inside.

There was enough fish in the pot to make a hearty supper for every member of the family, and they drank the broth afterwards. Nanow's spirits rose, and he made up a little song.

The hunters are in the forest.
They look for game to left, to right,
But nothing see,
And home come empty-handed.
Aya-ya, aya-ya, aya-ya!

The lake is cold and frozen,
No sign of life in sight.
But far below
Swim the big fish merrily.
Aya-ya, aya-ya, aya-ya!

The ice chisel breaks their house.
Ootook, the fisherman, drops her line.
With a nail for hook,
She fills the cooking pot.
Aya-ya, aya-ya, aya-ya!

Everyone had to laugh at Nanow's song, but Ootook felt very happy. And now, in the dim light of the stove, Aklunak told of the hunting trip. They had seen one caribou far off. Aklunak was so excited and anxious to get food that he shot too quickly. The bullet frightened the caribou so it ran a distance, and the second shot didn't go near it. Nanow had no chance to use his rifle, and they had seen no other game.

The whole household was up early next morning. After a breakfast of tea, Aklunak's few possessions were packed on Nanow's sled for the trip to Padlei. Yarrak made sure Ootook's fishing line was tucked in with the rest.

Yarrak and the two small children were bundled up in all the fur blankets, while Ootook and her sister ran alongside with Aklunak and Nanow. They changed places every now and then to rest, or get warm. The dogs ran happily, in spite of the heavier load, for they sensed that they were going home. Nanow stopped once to make tea at the wayside igloo he had built on the journey north.

It was long after dark when they reached Padlei. No lights showed at the trader's house or at Kretsuyuk's. Everyone had gone to bed long ago. But the dogs howled as they raced up the slope to the house and, a moment later, someone lighted a gas lamp inside.

What a happy homecoming! Eegie pressed her nose against Ootook's little button of a nose, and so did Tudlik. Shaunuk wakened and smiled, then promptly went back to sleep again. Everyone shook hands with everyone else, and sometimes twice, in their excitement. Then they settled down on the floor and benches. Eegie brought in some caribou meat from the porch, and Nanow hacked off bits with his

Eegie welcomes Ootook home with a quick brush of the nose.

axe. She dished out the stew left over from supper, and brought bannock from the food box. Oh, it felt wonderful to eat again, and to have as much as they liked.

Aklunak and Yarrak seemed a little shy at first. The light dazzled their eyes, and the warmth made them very sleepy. Eegie provided them with caribou skins and wool blankets, and they slept on the floor. It was much more comfortable than the drafty log hut.

In the morning, Aklunak went over to the store. To his surprise, he found that his Family Allowance credit had indeed grown during the past months. He was able to bring home a large supply of food for his family, and could get more later on. Aklunak decided to stay at Padlei for the rest of the winter. That afternoon, Nanow and Kretsuyuk helped him build his own snowhouse among the other igloos on the hillside.

After Aklunak and his family moved, Eegie fumbled among the bedding and brought out a beautiful white parka. "A girl could try this on," she said. That was her way of giving it to Ootook.

Ootook could hardly believe her eyes, but she put it on at once. She ran her hands over the velvety smooth white skin. The fur on the inside lay warm and smooth against her, and the tall narrow hood flopped over to one side, just as a Padleimiut woman's hood should.

"One would like to have beads for it," Eegie went on. "Perhaps that can be done later."

In the midst of her excitement, Ootook remembered her sister. "She has no warm clothing," she said thoughtfully. "Perhaps she would like my old parka. Then she will be able to come out and play."

Eegie smiled gently. "Perhaps she would like that."

At once, Ootook took her parka over to the new snowhouse where her sister lived now. She politely pretended the parka was no good. "A girl is growing too big for it," she said. But her sister was as pleased with it as Ootook was with her new white parka.

The next time Ootook visited her family, there was a brand new baby. Yarrak smiled at Ootook, as she showed her the baby born just that morning in the snowhouse.

"Another little brother for you," Yarrak said.

"Another hunter, when he grows up," said Ootook politely. She loved this baby brother at once, and would have carried him in the back of her new parka. But he was too young for that.

With plenty of food and warm outdoor clothing, Aklunak and Yarrak and the children grew stronger every day. Kretsuyuk had given his son Kingmik and another sled-dog, and Aklunak set a trapline east of Padlei, and was fairly successful. Yarrak learned to fish through the ice, like the women of the other igloos. After a few weeks, she looked as healthy as the woman on the Family Allowance poster, Ootook thought.

One day Nanow returned from his trapline with

Ootook's little sled upturned on his big sled. He had visited his trapline to the north, and this time brought in six foxes.

He handed one to Ootook. "That fox is yours," he said. Then he told the others, "Ootook found the right spot, and cut away the snow, and the fox stepped into the trap. So it is her fox."

Ootook couldn't pretend she didn't care. Her whole face beamed with happiness. "I will skin it myself, the way Tudlik does. Then I will scrape it clean, the way Eegie does. Then I will take it to the trader, the way Nanow does. And I will trade it for traps to catch more white foxes." She stopped, her black eyes shining.

Everyone laughed at Ootook's program.

"What would a girl do with many foxes?" Eegie asked.

Ootook was slowly learning to think of the needs of others, not always of herself. "The new baby brother will need many things," she said with dignity. "I will set my traps for him."

She was so busy for the next few days that she had no time to play with Mary. Word had been spread around that the doctor was coming to Padlei, and he wanted to see as many Eskimos as possible. So one morning when Ootook ran down to the playhouse, she met Mary, all dressed up in her white parka, beaded on the tall hood and around the shoulders.

Ootook in her old clothes meets Mary dressed in her prettiest parka beside their playhouse.

Mary's mother comes to tell them that the airplane will not arrive till the next day. Ootook admires this parka very much.

"The beautiful parka!" Ootook exclaimed. "One is dressed for a festival."

"The airplane is coming today," said Mary, importantly. "The doctor will be on it, and maybe other people. My mother is wearing her nice parka, too."

Just then Mary's mother came out of the house, and down the hill toward them. Rows of beads went around the hood and shoulders of her parka, the prettiest garment Ootook had ever seen.

"Word has just come over the radio-phone that the airplane will not arrive until tomorrow," she told them in Eskimo.

Mary's face looked sad. "Do I have to take off this parka?"

"Of course not," said her mother smiling.

Ootook couldn't help telling them about the new parka Eegie had made for her. "It's lovely white, like yours, but it hasn't got any beads on it."

Mary's mother smiled again. "We have beads in our house, and cloth to sew them on. If you and Mary would like to sew on beads, I will show you the patterns."

Ootook was delighted. Soon she and Mary were sitting on the red carpet of the living room. Ootook liked to bounce on the soft sofa, but when a person worked with beads, it was better to sit on the floor. The small beads looked so pretty lying on a white plate—red, black, blue, yellow, green, and pink. Ootook liked to roll the hard round little balls in the palms of her hands.

The beads were sewn first to a piece of black cloth. Then the cloth was sewn to the fur clothing. That way, the patches could easily be taken off old clothing and sewn to new garments. A long strip of beadwork was used to decorate the tall hood, with a large patch just above the face. Another band went around the shoulder, and sometimes loops of beads were left dangling.

It was important to take the beads in the right order, to form the pattern. Ootook and Mary threaded their needles with cotton because it was finer than sinew. Then the slim needles flashed in and out of the cloth, each stitch catching a bead into position. It took a lot of beads to make a pattern, and a lot of time, but Ootook enjoyed every moment of it.

As they sat there quietly, absorbed in their sewing, Mary suddenly said, "The next time the airplane comes it will be in summer, and it will land on the water of the lake. I will go away in it, Ootook, to school."

Ootook didn't know what school was, so Mary explained. "It's a place where you learn to read and write and add figures."

"But you already do those things," said Ootook.

"There are many other things I don't know," said Mary. She described the town where she would live, with all its houses and its hundreds of people. Ootook couldn't imagine any place with more than four buildings and ten snowhouses. How could there be enough caribou in one place to feed all those people?

Mary's mother sits on the carpet with the girls, showing them how to make beaded patterns for their clothing.

Then she thought how lonesome she would be when Mary was gone. Whom would she play with? Pana would go hunting and trapping with his father next winter. Shaunuk would play with the little brother. Why, of course, she remembered, she had her new sister.

Mary's mother said comfortingly, "Never mind, it is not for a long time yet. Just think, the nice summer will be here before then. Summer—when the birds and the caribou come back, and the land is covered with little flowers. Summer—when we don't have to wear fur clothing every time we go out."

"Summer is when the mosquitoes are thick," Mary said with a giggle.

"Winter is the best time," said Ootook. "Then one can travel around the country." They laughed, remembering her travels. "And besides, in winter one can have a trapline for white foxes."

That was the most important thing of all. Suddenly it seemed to Ootook that work was more interesting than play. She wasn't sure whether sewing beads would be called work or play. She knew she enjoyed it.

After several hours, Ootook finished one large pattern, and Mary completed two small ones. Then her mother gathered up the materials and put them away. She gave Ootook the pieces the girls had beaded, and some others that she took from her sewing box.

"These are for your new parka, Ootook," she said.

"Eegie will sew them on for you. Now you girls have been indoors long enough. Perhaps you would like to play outdoors for a while." As they went through the kitchen, she added, "And here is a candy apiece."

Ootook loved candy, but she didn't have it very often. At once she popped the piece into her mouth. It was hard, and would last a long time. Then she remembered her little brother who had never tasted candy.

"The small brother would like this," she told Mary. They hurried across the lake to the snowhouse. No one had ever told Ootook about germs, and her little brother had never heard of them either. Ootook took the candy out of her mouth, and put it in his. "One does not swallow it," she warned. "It is to enjoy in the mouth."

The three-year-old brother looked at her solemnly at first. Then his eyes lighted up, and she saw that he liked candy just as much as she did.

The airplane lands on skis on the frozen lake in front of the Padlei trading post.

Chapter Nine

THE DRUM DANCE

A few more Eskimos arrived at Padlei that night, to be there for the doctor's visit. Some built themselves snowhouses on the hill, while others stayed at Kretsuyuk's house.

Eegie sewed the beaded patches on Ootook's new white parka, and secretly took some strips off her own. It was beautiful, Ootook thought. Since the doctor was to arrive that day, she put on the white parka first thing. Everybody dressed in their finest clothing for his visit, and the drum dance that would follow.

About noon, the children playing outside the igloos heard a droning sound, above the whir of the windchargers. They shrieked in excitement, and that brought their parents out to look. The droning grew steadily louder, and the airplane came in sight over the low hills. It circled around the trading post, then landed on the frozen lake. With snow spraying up from its skiis, it carved two broad tracks across the lake.

Every person in Padlei gathered around to watch the passengers come out of the aircraft. The pilot jumped out of one door, and the doctor climbed carefully down on the other side.

They both shook hands with everyone, then car-

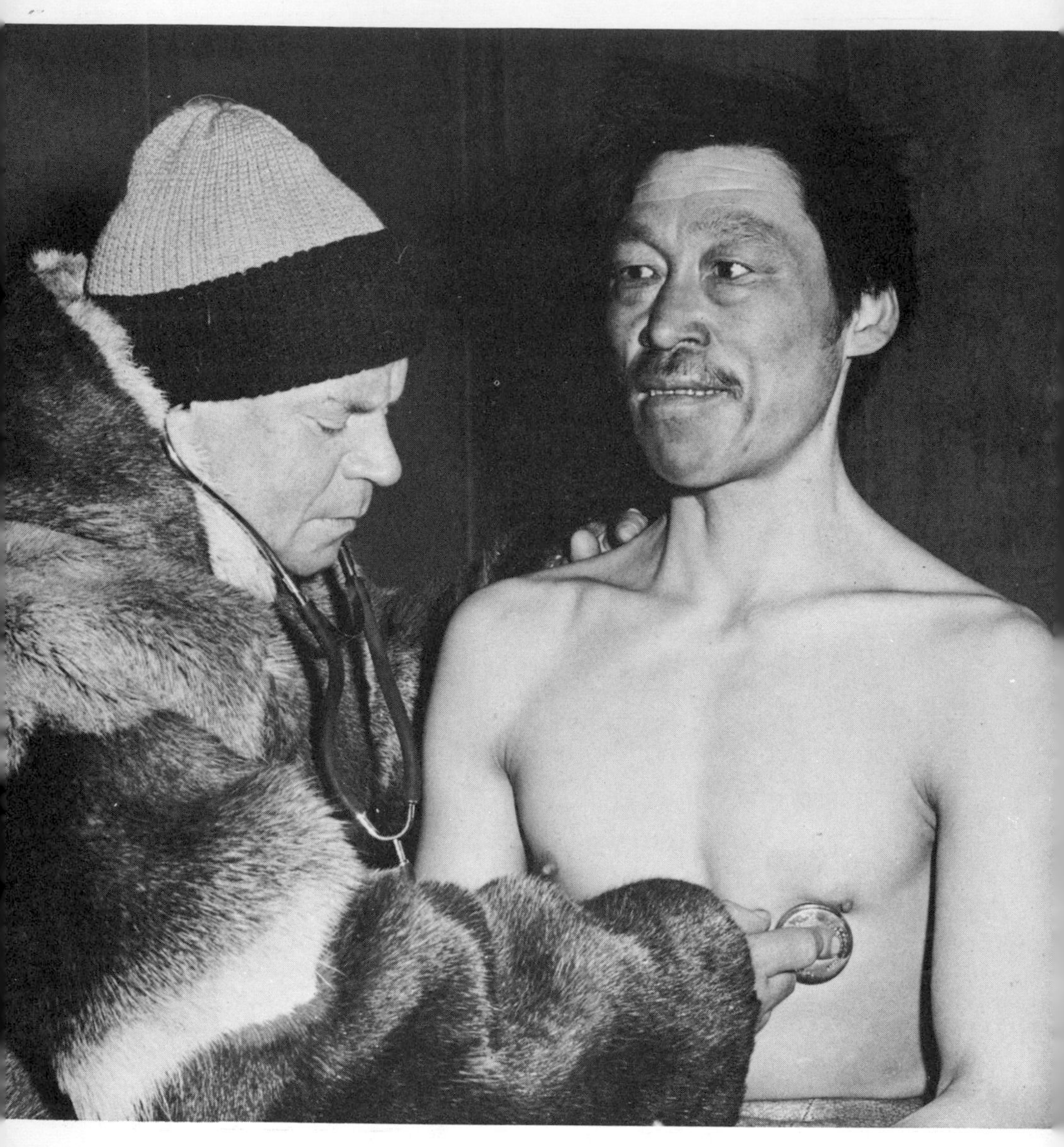

The doctor uses a stethoscope to listen to Aklunak's heart-beat.

ried their bags up to the trader's house. Kretsuyuk carried up other boxes and bundles, with Pana helping him. The pilot soon came back to take care of his plane. He didn't want Pana and the other boys climbing inside it.

About an hour later, the doctor was ready to inspect the Eskimos. He came over to Kretsuyuk's house, and between them, they managed to make everyone understand what the doctor wanted. This doctor did the strangest things, Ootook thought, as she sat on the sleeping bench watching every move.

He told Eegie to open her mouth wide, while he looked inside with a little light. Why did the doctor do that? Ootook wondered. Eegie's teeth were strong, though worn down by many years of softening leather. Ootook understood later, when the doctor had to pull an aching tooth for another patient.

Then he told Aklunak to pull off his parka. The doctor put a little metal plate against Aklunak's chest, and stuck two things into his own ears. If he had told Ootook that he was listening to Aklunak's heartbeat, she would have been even more puzzled. He put the same disk against the new baby's heart, and smiled. "A fine healthy baby," he said, in his few words of Eskimo.

And the doctor would often pick up an eyelid, and look under it. What was hidden there? Ootook tried to see for herself. The most fascinating thing the doctor did was to prick everyone's arms with a shiny needle. "This will prevent measles," he said.

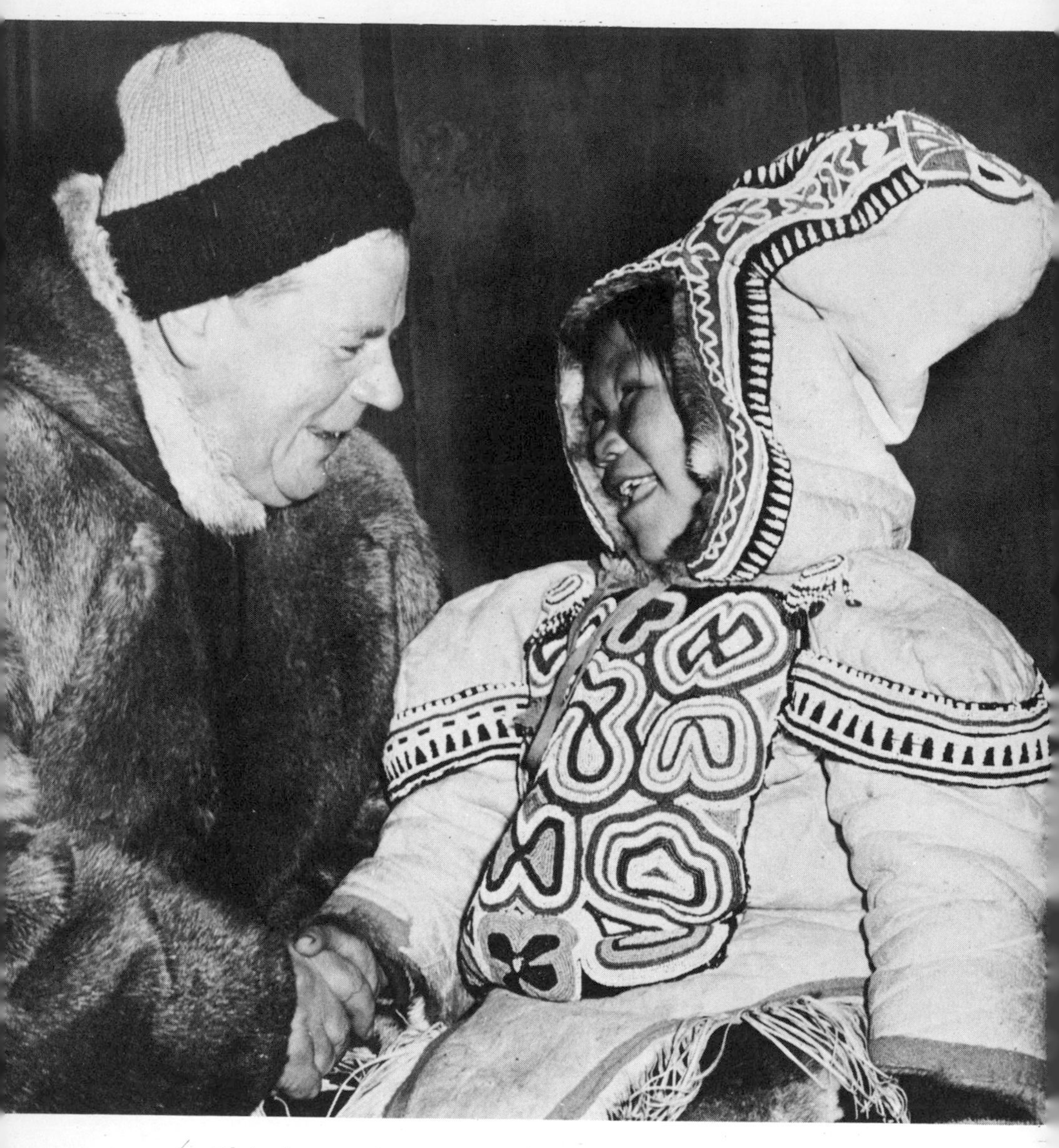

The doctor shakes Ootook's hand and tells her she is a brave girl.

Many Eskimos had died of measles, and Ootook was glad when her turn came. But when the doctor told her to take off her nice new parka, she obeyed very slowly. The doctor understood and smiled. Then he pricked her arm with the needle, and she found it didn't hurt at all.

"You are a brave girl," said the doctor, shaking hands again.

Ootook didn't know what he was saying, but it sounded nice, so she gave him a wide smile in return.

The stream of Eskimos to Kretsuyuk's house ended only when suppertime came and the doctor went back to the trader's house. He would finish his medical examinations the next day.

During the afternoon Nanow had prepared the drum for singing and dancing that evening. A caribou skin, scraped free of hair and fat, was stretched over a circular frame of willow. He tied the parchment in place, winding cord around the frame. Then he pulled the skin very tight, so that it made a loud rolling sound when he struck the edge with a drumstick.

Soon after supper, the Eskimos drifted back into the house, and squatted on the floor or on benches. Ootook and Shaunuk were excited with so much company. Aklunak and Yarrak came with their new baby. Karluk and his family were in from the camp out to the southwest. Pana was there with his parents, as well as neighbors from around Padlei, and other Eskimos whom Ootook did not know. Some of the

Nanow tightens the caribou hide over the wooden frame, to make the drum ready.

women brought their babies, and a few young children played around on the floor.

Finally an old man took the drum by the handle. He struck the frame a few times, then stopped. "I cannot drum," he said. He was displaying good manners.

"You are a fine drummer," the others assured him. He tried again. "No I am no good." They urged him, and at last be began to sing his song, and beat the drum. At the end of the verse, his wife and the other women sitting around took up the chorus, "Aya-ya, aya-ya, aya-ya." They swayed as they sang, with their eyes half shut.

Ootook sang the chorus along with the women, for the words and tune were easy. Then the old man ended. He gave the drum a little tap, laid it and the stick on the floor, and stepped back to his seat against the wall.

Then the next oldest man in the group was coaxed to sing and dance. It was then Kretsuyuk's turn.

"No, no," he protested, "I have no songs." Ootook knew he had several songs, and nearly spoke out loud. But she realized, in time, that her grandfather was just being polite.

He stepped into the middle of the floor and took up the drum, struck it once or twice on the wooden frame. Then he stopped. "It is not a good song. It is an old one I made long ago, when I used to hunt caribou."

Ootook's grin stretched all across her face. That

Kretsuyuk said he had no song, but he sang and danced.
Shaunuk looks at him from the wall.

was her favorite song, one he had often sung to her. So when he started to chant, so did she. Eegie and some other women took up the song, too, all swaying together.

Kretsuyuk sang:

Aya ya, aya ya,
It came right in my way,
The caribou cow with its calf,
Near the margin of a lake,
Aya ya, aya ya, aya ya.

He struck the drum frame with the stick, and it swung around wildly, its shadow leaping on the wall of the house, He seemed to forget the people around him as he sang and danced, and to live through the hunt all over again as he swayed to and fro with each beat of the drum.

So also came right in my way,
The bull with the mighty antlers,
By the margin of a lake.
My doing it was that it never again
Went a-wandering.
Aya ya, aya ya, aya ya.

Kretsuyuk's song went on for several more verses, reminding everyone that he had been a great hunter in his youth. He was very hot and tired when his song ended, and he laid the drum on the floor.

Several other men took up the drum in their turn. Nanow sang a funny song that had everyone laughing till the tears rolled down their cheeks. Then it was Aklunak's turn. Ootook watched her father, wondering what he would sing. He couldn't sing about his bad luck. Only a very successful hunter could do that, pretending to be a poor hunter.

Aklunak surprised them all with a song he had made up that afternoon. It was about the airplane. He had taught his wife, and Yarrak had taught some of the other women.

Aklunak took up the drum and began:

A buzzing in the air,
Is it a mosquito? Is it a bumblebee?
No!

"*Hayai-ya, hayai-ya,*" sang the women.

Louder it sounds,
The drone fills my ears.
Is it a bird that flies?
No!

"*Hayai-ya, hayai-ya,*" came the chorus.

Up in the sky
It sails on the wind.
Does it flap its wings?
No!

"Hayai-ya, hayai-ya," the women chanted.

Like a duck it lands.
The snow scatters far.
It is the white man's bird!
Yes!

"Hayai-ya, hayai-ya," came the chant from all around the room, and Ootook sang loudest of all. She was proud of Aklunak.

The songs went on, hour after hour. Ootook knew that Pana would not sing a song, because he was still too young. He had not yet killed a caribou. When he did, he too would make a song for the dance festival.

The little house grew hot, with so many people in it, and the air was thick with tobacco smoke. Ootook found it hard to keep her eyes open, and she noticed that Shaunuk had already fallen asleep. Ootook yawned. Then she pulled off the beaded white parka she had worn all day, and put it away carefully in the corner.

Shaunuk woke up suddenly, and she crawled under the caribou skin blanket with Ootook, at one end of the sleeping bench. She clutched in her arms Mary's doll with the black hair.

The throb of the drum and the monotonous chant seemed to weave in and out of Ootook's thoughts . . . the doctor's visit . . . "aya ya" . . . her new family . . . the trapline . . . "aya ya" . . . She would trap many foxes, so that they need never go

Ootook and Shaunuk under the caribou skin blankets, with Mary's dark-haired doll.

hungry again. Aklunak and Yarrak could have the Family Allowance for her.

But for all that, this was her real family—Kretsuyuk and Eegie, Nanow and Tudlik and Shaunuk. "It is good that one does not have to go away from one's family the way Mary will do," she thought drowsily . . . and that was the last she remembered. Ootook was sound asleep.

CADMUS
BOOKS